Laura Ingalls Wilder

Leslie Strudwick

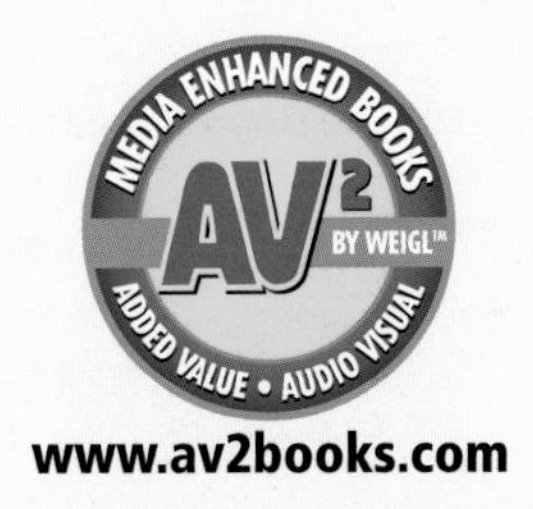

www.av2books.com

Go to www.av2books.com, and enter this book's unique code.

BOOK CODE

V669491

AV² by Weigl brings you media enhanced books that support active learning.

AV² provides enriched content that supplements and complements this boo
Weigl's AV² books strive to create inspired learning and engage young min
in a total learning experience.

Your AV² Media Enhanced books come alive with...

Audio
Listen to sections of the book read aloud.

Key Words
Study vocabulary, and complete a matching word activity.

Video
Watch informative video clips.

Quizzes
Test your knowledge.

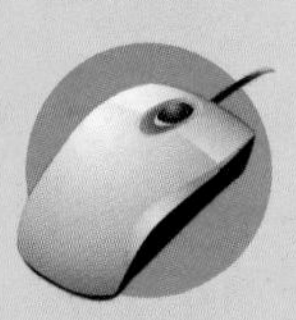

Embedded Weblinks
Gain additional information for research.

Slide Show
View images and captions, and prepare a presentation.

Try This!
Complete activities and hands-on experiments.

... and much, much more

Published by AV² by Weigl
350 5th Avenue, 59th Floor
New York, NY 10118

Website: www.weigl.com www.av2books.com

Library of Congress Control Number: 2013953123

ISBN 978-1-4896-0660-0 (hardcover)
ISBN 978-1-4896-0661-7 (softcover)
ISBN 978-1-4896-0662-4 (single-user eBook)
ISBN 978-1-4896-0663-1 (multi-user eBook)

Printed in the United States of America, in North Mankato, Minnesota
1 2 3 4 5 6 7 8 9 0 18 17 16 15 14

012014
WEP301113

Senior Editor: Heather Kissock
Design: Terry Paulhus

Weigl acknowledges Getty Images, Alamy, Harper Collins, Laura Ingalls Wilder Home and Museum, Dreamstime, and Newscom as its primary photo suppliers for this title.

Contents

Introducing Laura Ingalls Wilder

The best way to learn about Laura Ingalls Wilder is to read her Little House books. These books describe the pioneer life of Laura and her family on the American prairies in the late 1800s. It was not until Laura was about 60 years of age that she began to write about her experiences. By then, the days of frontier living had long passed. Laura realized that **homesteading** on the prairies had been a very interesting and special way of life. She decided to write about her past so her own daughter would know what homesteading was like. Laura also fondly remembered the stories her mother and father used to tell about their childhoods. She wanted those stories to be remembered, too.

Laura had a special connection with her fans. She enjoyed meeting them at book fairs and book signings.

Like other American homesteaders, the Ingalls family traveled the prairies in a horse-drawn covered wagon, much like the one on display at the Laura Ingalls Wilder Museum in Walnut Grove, Minnesota.

The characters Ma and Pa are known to millions of children around the world who have read the Little House books. Ma and Pa were actually Laura Ingalls Wilder's parents, Caroline and Charles Ingalls.

Charles had an adventurous spirit and wanted to be a **homesteader**. Caroline shared her husband's dream to travel west and break new farmland. Her only insistence was that their children receive an education no matter where they settled. The adventures of the Ingalls and their family have been retold in Laura Ingalls Wilder's Little House series.

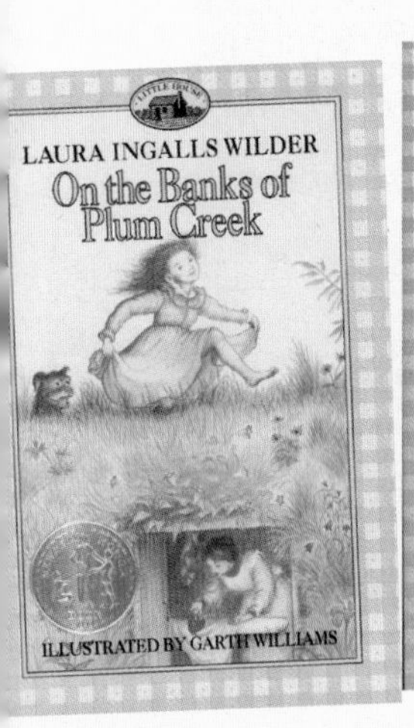

Writing A Biography

Writers are often inspired to record the stories of people who lead interesting lives. The story of another person's life is called a biography. A biography can tell the story of any person, from authors such as Laura Ingalls Wilder, to inventors, presidents, and sports stars.

When writing a biography, authors must first collect information about their subject. This information may come from a book about the person's life, a news article about one of his or her accomplishments, or a review of his or her work. Libraries and the internet will have much of this information. Most biographers will also interview their subjects. Personal accounts provide a great deal of information and a unique point of view. When some basic details about the person's life have been collected, it is time to begin writing a biography.

As you read about Laura Ingalls Wilder, you will be introduced to the important parts of a biography. Use these tips and the examples provided to learn how to write about an author or any other remarkable person.

Early Life

The Ingalls had their first child, Mary, in 1865. Laura Elizabeth was born two years later, near Pepin, Wisconsin. The two sisters were **inseparable**. When Laura was about 2 years old, Ma and Pa packed their covered wagon and moved from their farm in Pepin. They headed toward Kansas. It was a long and difficult journey. Much later in her life, Laura wrote a book about the trip called *Little House on the Prairie*.

"The Little House books are stories of long ago. The way we live is much different now, and so many changes have made living and learning easier."
— *Laura Ingalls Wilder*

Kansas was a good place to start a homestead. Once a family laid claim to a piece of land, built a home on it, and worked on it for five years, the land belonged to them. The Ingalls loved the openness of the prairies. They built their homestead near a bustling new town called Independence.

A replica of the log cabin Laura lived in can be found near Wayside, Kansas, about 7 miles (11 kilometers) north of Pepin.

Ma and Pa worked hard to build their home and farm the land. Mary and Laura were still quite young, but they pitched in whenever they could. They had time to play, too. It was not long before the two sisters welcomed a new playmate. Little sister Carrie was born in the summer of 1870.

When American homesteaders moved to Kansas, much of the land belonged to the Native Americans. The Native Americans were willing to share their land as long as they could maintain their own way of life. However, the settlers' arrival soon changed things. There were fewer animals for the Native Americans to hunt and less land available to them. In an effort to preserve their land and their way of life, the Native Americans asked the settlers to leave Kansas. As a result, the Ingalls family moved in the fall of 1870.

Carrie, Mary, and Laura were very close. They did their chores together and played together in their spare time.

Writing About Early Life

A person's early years have a strong influence on his or her future. Parents, teachers, and friends can have a large impact on how a person thinks, feels, and behaves. These effects are strong enough to last throughout childhood, and often a person's lifetime.

In order to write about a person's early life, biographers must find answers to the following questions.

1. Where and when was the person born?
2. What is known about the person's family and friends?
3. Did the person grow up in unusual circumstances?

Growing Up

Pa decided that the family should return to the farm in Pepin, Wisconsin. Laura was 4 years old at the time. She fondly remembered the journey, with the scent of the prairie flowers, the swaying of the wagon, and Pa's stories and fiddle playing. Pa's stories fascinated Laura. Her love for listening to and telling stories began at an early age.

Pa farmed the land in Wisconsin for two years. During that time, he dreamed of going back west. In the spring of 1873, Pa sold the farm and headed west with his family. This time, the Ingalls stopped in Minnesota.

Laura's love for listening to and telling stories began at an early age.

Ma and Pa bought 172 acres of farmland near Walnut Grove, Minnesota. In Laura's books, Walnut Grove is known as Plum Creek. The family's first home was a **sod dugout** built into a riverbank. It was a little dusty, but it was home. The family lived there while Pa built them a house.

Get to Know Minnesota

The family quickly settled into life in Walnut Grove and became part of the growing community. Laura made friends with children and adults alike. Later, she wrote about the people of this community in the book, *On the Banks of Plum Creek*.

In 1875, the family moved into their new home. In November of the same year, a little boy named Charles Frederick was born. The crops were growing well, but the good fortune did not last long. A **plague** of grasshoppers destroyed the family's wheat crop. Left without a crop, Pa was forced to take a job in town. He met a man, Mr. Steadman, who was moving to Iowa to operate a hotel. He asked Charles and his family to move to Iowa to oversee the operation of the hotel.

Visitors to the Laura Ingalls Wilder Museum in Walnut Grove, Minnesota, can view a variety of historical items from Laura's life.

Writing About Growing Up

Some people know what they want to achieve in life from a very young age. Others do not decide until much later. In any case, it is important for biographers to discuss when and how their subjects make these decisions. Using the information they collect, biographers try to answer the following questions about their subjects' paths in life.

1. Who had the most influence on the person?
2. Did he or she receive assistance from others?
3. Did the person have a positive attitude?

Developing Skills

The trip to Iowa was a very sad one. Ma and Pa had wanted to move west, not east. To make matters worse, little Charles Frederick, nicknamed "Freddie," was very sick. Despite the efforts of a doctor, Freddie died. The Ingalls were devastated. After a long and dreary journey, they arrived in Burr Oak, Iowa.

"We'll always be farmers, for what is bred in the bone will come out in the flesh."
—Laura Ingalls Wilder

The Ingalls family moved into a back room of the hotel. Laura and her sisters were very busy. They attended school and helped their parents by doing chores around the hotel. The Ingalls did not like living in the tiny hotel room. Pa soon found a brick house for them on the outskirts of town.

From left to right, this Ingalls family portrait shows Ma, Carrie, Laura, Pa, Grace, and Mary.

Laura never wrote about the town of Burr Oak. However, Burr Oak is where Laura learned to read. She was always grateful to her teacher, Mr. Reed, for teaching her to read. Laura loved reading poetry. Often, she would **recite** poems to her parents.

The Ingalls welcomed another girl, Grace, into the family before they packed their bags and moved again. This time, they returned to Walnut Grove, Minnesota. Laura went back to school.

At 14 years of age, Mary became very sick. The doctor diagnosed her with **meningitis**. The sickness left Mary visually impaired. From then on, Laura acted as her sister's eyes. She described everything that she saw to Mary.

In 1881, Mary Ingalls began attending the Iowa Braille and Sight Saving School located in Vinton, Iowa, an institution for students who are legally blind. She finished her schooling there in 1889.

Writing About Developing Skills

Every remarkable person has skills and traits that make him or her noteworthy. Some people have natural talent, while others practice diligently. For most, it is a combination of the two. One of the most important things that a biographer can do is to tell the story of how the subject developed his or her talents.

1. What was the person's education?
2. What was the person's first job or work experience?
3. What obstacles did the person overcome?

Timeline of Laura Ingalls Wilder

1867

Laura is born in a log cabin near Pepin, Wisconsin on February 7. Two years later, the Ingalls family moves to Kansas.

1870

Laura's sister Carrie is born, and the family moves back to Wisconsin.

1874

Laura and her family move to Walnut Grove, Minnesota.

1875

The Ingalls move to Burr Oak, Iowa, where Ma and Pa operate a hotel.

1879

The Ingalls family moves to De Smet, North Dakota.

1883

Laura begins teaching in a nearby village.

1885
Laura marries Almanzo Wilder and moves to his farm.

1886
Laura and Almanzo's daughter, Rose, is born.

1894
Laura, Almanzo, and Rose move to Mansfield, Missouri. The family buys a farm called Rocky Ridge.

1932
Laura's first book, *Little House in the Big Woods*, is released.

1957
Laura Ingalls Wilder dies at 90 years of age.

Early Achievements

Pa still did not want to give up his dream of moving west and farming. However, he realized that his family was settled in Walnut Grove. So, Charles packed up the covered wagon and headed off on his own to look for land. It took some time, but the rest of the family eventually joined him in De Smet, South Dakota. Laura wrote about this journey in *By the Shores of Silver Lake*. The Ingalls embraced De Smet as their home. Four of Laura Ingalls Wilder's books are set in this town, including *The Long Winter*.

"Pa and Ma were great readers, and I read a lot at home with them."
—Laura Ingalls Wilder

Before Laura even finished school, a man from a nearby village approached Pa and asked if Laura would teach at their schoolhouse. Laura was only 15 years old at the time. She did not want to leave home, but she knew that the money would help her family.

At first, Laura was very lonely. Her loneliness was eased when a friend from De Smet, Almanzo Wilder, began giving her rides home for the weekend. Laura and Almanzo's friendship grew during these trips. She began calling Almanzo "Manly," and he nicknamed Laura "Bess."

The Ingalls Homestead is located about 1 mile (1.6 km) outside De Smet, South Dakota. Laura lived on the homestead for five years, leaving when she married Almanzo.

On August 25, 1885, Laura and Almanzo were married. Laura joined him on his farm. A year after they were married, the couple had a baby girl. Laura named her Rose after the wild roses that grew on the prairies.

While Laura and Almanzo were happy with their new child, times were tough, and money was **scarce**. The year following Rose's birth, the Wilder's crops failed to grow. Then, both Laura and Almanzo became ill with **diphtheria**. Laura recovered, but the disease caused permanent damage to Almanzo's legs. He needed a cane to walk.

A second baby was born in 1889, but sadly, he only survived a few days. Just when it seemed that things could not get worse, the Wilder's house burned down. Laura wrote about this difficult period many years later, but she hid the **manuscript**. It was found and published after her death.

Almanzo and Laura decided to move. The family settled in Mansfield, Missouri. They bought a farm and named it Rocky Ridge.

Almanzo Wilder was 10 years older than Laura. The two courted for two-and-a-half years before getting married.

Writing About Early Achievements

No two people take the same path to success. Some people work very hard for a long time before achieving their goals. Others may take advantage of a fortunate turn of events. Biographers must make special note of the traits and qualities that allow their subjects to succeed.

1. What was the person's most important early success?
2. What processes does the person use in his or her work?
3. Which of the person's traits was most helpful in his or her work?

Tricks of the Trade

Laura Ingalls Wilder thought writing was like using "word pictures." It was a way to remember and explain details of her life, to tell a story, and to keep a memory alive. Read on to find out how Laura Ingalls Wilder turned her pioneer experiences into popular books that have become classics.

Create "Word Pictures"

Laura began creating "word pictures" when her sister Mary became ill and was left visually impaired. Laura used words to describe the world around her so that Mary would know about her surroundings. Laura explained everything in great detail. She was constantly learning new words and developing her **vocabulary**. Descriptive writing can be improved by the use of interesting and uncommon words. New writers can develop their vocabulary by keeping a dictionary and looking up words that are new to them.

Laura continued her storytelling when her daughter Rose was born. Rose later became a writer herself and is believed to have encouraged her mother to write her stories in book form.

Tell Stories

One of the reasons Laura Ingalls Wilder began writing books was to **preserve** and share her experiences. She thought that by writing about her life, others would learn about pioneer times. She also wanted to write books so that Rose could enjoy Pa's stories. Pa's pioneering stories were kept alive through Laura's books. New writers can share and gather stories, too. One way new writers can share stories is by gathering family members together in a sharing circle. Often, an older family member can contribute interesting stories about his or her own childhood. Writing those stories down on paper is the next step. Laura Ingalls Wilder thought that her childhood was dull until she wrote about it and realized that many people found her past interesting. A descriptive storyteller can often make any story come to life.

"We who live in quiet places have the opportunity to become acquainted with ourselves, to think our own thoughts and live our own lives in a way that is not possible for those keeping up with the crowd."
—*Laura Ingalls Wilder*

Laura spent most of her time writing the *Little House on the Prairie* books at the desk in her Mansfield, Missouri, home.

Remarkable Books

Laura's Little House series of books originally began as just one book, *Pioneer Girl*. The publisher thought the book was too long to be published as one book. Laura reworked the manuscript to create several books. Each book continues the story of Laura's life, from the time she was a little girl until she was married and raising her own little girl.

Little House in the Big Woods

Any boy or girl who has dreamed about living in the deep, dark forest will enjoy reading this book. In *Little House in the Big Woods*, Laura is about 5 years of age. She lives with her family in a small house in Wisconsin. She and her sister, Mary, love to sit on Pa's knee and listen to his stories. The family faces many hardships, such as a bitter Wisconsin snowstorm and a panther attack. Laura learns how to be a pioneer girl, helping Ma out with chores, such as butter churning, and watching over her little sister, Carrie.

Little House on the Prairie

When the Ingalls family leaves their cozy house in the big woods of Wisconsin, they embark on a grand adventure. *Little House on the Prairie* is perhaps the best-known of Laura's books. Its popularity is partly due to the television series of the same name. In the book, the Ingalls travel across the prairies in a covered wagon for many days. They settle when they find a good location to farm and build their house. This book traces and describes the family's move from Wisconsin to Kansas. People will love reading about Laura's pioneering days.

On the Banks of Plum Creek

In this book, the Ingalls family leave their little house on the prairie in their covered wagon. They embark on a long journey, headed toward Minnesota. When they arrive, the family finds a good place to settle and builds a sod house. They live near the beautiful banks of Plum Creek. Pa works night and day to build a larger home made from lumber. Before long, Pa completes a wonderful house with glass windows and a hinged door. Laura and her sister go to school, help with the chores, and fish in the creek. Pa's fiddle music keeps the entire family entertained in the evenings. Trouble visits the Ingalls more than once in the story. A grasshopper plague and a terrible blizzard are just some of the hardships the Ingalls must overcome. The family remains strong and works together through these difficult times.

AWARDS
On the Banks of Plum Creek
1938 Honor Book for the Newbery Medal

Farmer Boy

Almanzo Wilder, Laura's husband, grew up on a big farm in the state of New York. He spent his boyhood on the farm with his mother, father, brother, and two sisters. Almanzo told Laura the stories of his childhood, such as what it was like to work at farm chores from dusk to dawn. Later, Laura wrote about Almanzo's boyhood experiences in the book, *Farmer Boy*. Although Almanzo's family were hardworking farmers, they still found time for fun. Almanzo loved horses and would head to the horse barn after chores were done. As a child, he would dream of the day that he would have a horse of his own.

The Long Winter

The adventures of Laura Ingalls and her family continue as Pa, Ma, Laura, Mary, Carrie, and little Grace bravely face a bitterly cold winter in the Dakota Territory. One blizzard after another hits De Smet, covering the town with snow and cutting off all outside supplies. Wood, food, and fuel are in short supply. As a result, there is almost no food left. Almanzo Wilder and a friend decide to make the difficult and dangerous trip across the prairie to find some wheat so that the people of De Smet will not starve.

AWARDS
The Long Winter
1941 Honor Book for the Newbery Medal

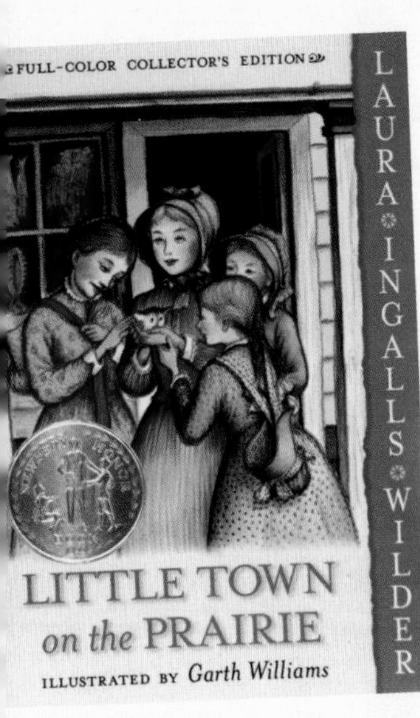

Little Town on the Prairie

AWARDS
Little Town on the Prairie
1942 Honor Book for the Newbery Medal

After the long, hard winter of 1880 to 1881, the town of De Smet is bustling with activity. Laura earns money to help send her sister, Mary, to a school for the visually impaired. Laura is also growing up. She receives her teaching certificate. She also has many new friends. However, Laura's **rival**, Nellie Oleson, moves to town. Despite Laura's attempts to forge a friendship with Nellie, the girls remain enemies. Laura attends many of the social activities in the town, including an evening social. Best of all, Almanzo Wilder asks permission to walk home from church with Laura.

These Happy Golden Years

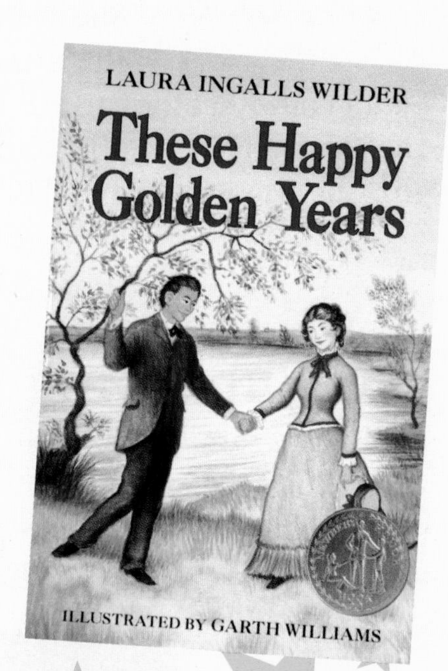

At only 15 years of age, Laura finds a teaching job that takes her away from her family and the town of De Smet. Since Laura has never lived away from her Ma and Pa, she is very homesick. To make matters worse, she shares lodgings with a woman who seems to dislike her. To help ease Laura's loneliness, Almanzo comes to get her every weekend to take her back to her family in De Smet. Over time, Laura's relationship with Almanzo grows. Readers will be fascinated to find out how the last book in the Little House series ends.

AWARDS
These Happy Golden Years
1944 Honor Book for the Newbery Medal

From Big Ideas to Books

Most of Laura's life was filled with daily farm chores. She loved living on the farm and worked hard. Although Laura was educated, had been a teacher, and enjoyed reading, she never really thought about becoming a writer. It was her daughter, Rose, who encouraged her mother to write. In 1915, when Laura was about 48 years of age, she went to San Francisco to visit Rose. Laura wrote Almanzo many letters about the trip. Almanzo kept all of these letters, and they eventually became Laura's last book, *West from Home*.

"I am beginning to learn that it is the sweet, simple things of life which are the real ones after all."
—Laura Ingalls Wilder

While in San Francisco, Rose told Laura that she should devote herself to writing. Laura began writing for local newspapers and magazines. She even had her own column in the Missouri Ruralist called "As a Farm Woman Thinks."

Laura knew that the early days of pioneering were over in America. She wanted to remember and preserve her experiences as a pioneer girl. She also wanted her daughter to know about her life.

The Publishing Process

Publishing companies receive hundreds of manuscripts from authors each year. Only a few manuscripts become books. Publishers must be sure that a manuscript will sell many copies. As a result, publishers reject most of the manuscripts they receive. Once a manuscript has been accepted, it goes through

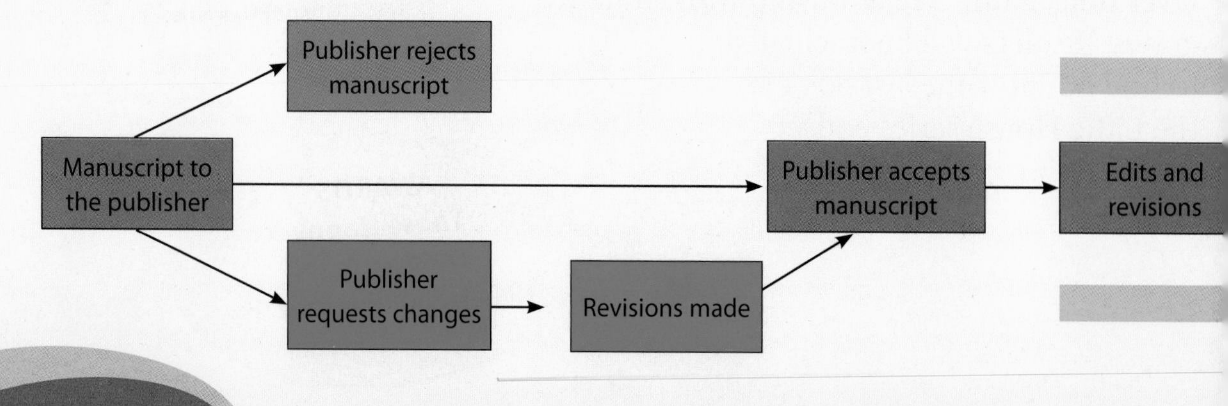

In 1930, Laura began writing about her days as a pioneer girl. She had an ability to remember the details of her past. Before long, Laura sent her writing to a publisher. The publisher said that the entire story would not fit into just one book. The story would have to be published as a series. The first book of the series was called *Little House in the Big Woods*. Laura said the first book was a tribute to her father, who had died years earlier. She was amazed by the popularity of the book. Children wrote to Laura and begged her to write more stories about life on the prairies.

Laura and Almanzo's Rocky Ridge Farmhouse in Mansfield, Missouri, is now a historic site and museum. More than 30,000 fans from across the United States and around the world visit the site each year.

Laura decided to write about Almanzo's childhood next. *Farmer Boy* was released in 1933. After that, she dedicated herself to writing, and six more books were published over the next 10 years. Three books were published after Laura's death.

many stages before it is published. Often, authors change their work to follow an editor's suggestions. Once the book is published, some authors receive royalties. This is money based on book sales.

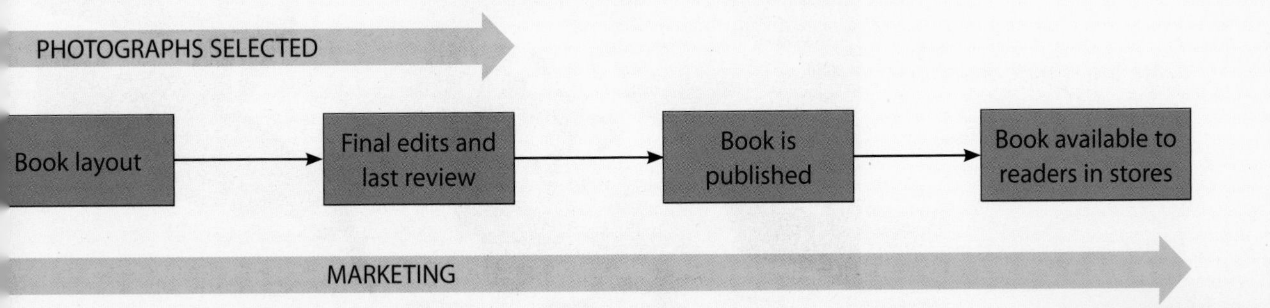

Laura Ingalls Wilder Today

Although Laura died in 1957, her memory is kept alive through her books and her dedicated readers. During the 1970s and early 1980s, a television program was aired based on one of Laura's books—*Little House on the Prairie*. It was one of the most popular shows on television. By watching this program, people around the world grew to love Laura Ingalls Wilder.

Towns with a connection to Laura Ingalls Wilder share their pride through museums and festivals. Many of them have festivals to celebrate their presence in American **literary** history. Museums can be found in towns such as Walnut Grove, De Smet, and Mansfield. In De Smet, visitors can explore the family's house. They can also see a **replica** of the family's log cabin near Pepin, or take a look at Almanzo's boyhood home in Malone, New York.

The Little House on the Prairie television show aired for nine seasons. Melissa Gilbert played the role of Laura.

Some Laura Ingalls Wilder fans have followed the path the Ingalls took in their journeys. They begin their trip in Wisconsin, drive to Kansas, visit Burr Oak in Iowa, and eventually end up in De Smet. In Walnut Grove, there is a Wilder Pageant which features the Laura Look-A-Like Contest. Pepin, Wisconsin hosts Laura Ingalls Wilder Days each September.

In 1954, three years before Laura's death, she was given the Laura Ingalls Wilder Award by the American Library Association. The award that bears her name continues to be given to authors or illustrators whose books have made significant contributions to children's literature in the United States.

Today, the Ingalls Homestead in De Smet provides people with an opportunity to experience pioneer life. Visitors can enjoy horse-drawn wagon rides and other pioneer activities.

Writing About the Person Today

The biography of any living person is an ongoing story. People have new ideas, start new projects, and deal with challenges. For their work to be meaningful, biographers must include up-to-date information about their subjects. Through research, biographers try to answer the following questions.

1. Has the person received awards or recognition for accomplishments?
2. What is the person's life's work?
3. How have the person's accomplishments served others?

Fan Information

After Laura's first book was published, she was surprised to find that she had attracted many fans. Children from across the United States wrote to her asking her to write more pioneering stories. Devoted readers continued to write to Laura over the years. She always tried to reply to each letter personally. Many of the letters were from children, but Laura also received letters from adults who had grown up reading her books and remained devoted fans. Eventually, Laura began to receive so many letters that she was no longer able to reply to them all.

Pioneer life continues to fascinate people of all ages. Re-enactments let people dress up in pioneer clothing and live like a pioneer for a day.

Some of Laura Ingalls Wilder's fans not only wrote to her, but dropped in to visit her at Rocky Ridge Farm. Laura considered visiting fans to be friends. She often invited them in for a cup of tea. Today, fans can still visit Rocky Ridge Farm. It has been preserved as part of the Save America's Treasures National Trust, and remains the same as it was in 1957. Visitors can tour the Wilder's house, see the furniture that Almanzo built, and wander around the grounds and the museum that has been built on the property.

Fans of Laura Ingalls Wilder can learn more about this wonderful author through Web sites on the Internet. Fans and historians have created many different sites in her memory.

The Laura Ingalls Wilder site gives people the opportunity to learn more about the author, her family, and her writings.

Write a Biography

All of the parts of a biography work together to tell the story of a person's life. Find out how these elements combine by writing a biography. Begin by choosing a person whose story fascinates you. You will have to research the person's life by using library books and reliable websites. You can also e-mail the person or write him or her a letter. The person might agree to answer your questions directly.

Use a concept web, such as the one below, to guide you in writing the biography. Answer each of the questions listed using the information you have gathered. Each heading on the concept web will form an important part of the person's story.

Parts of a Biography

Early Life

Where and when was the person born?

What is known about the person's family and friends?

Did the person grow up in unusual circumstances?

Growing Up

Who had the most influence on the person?

Did he or she receive assistance from others?

Did the person have a positive attitude?

Developing Skills

What was the person's education?

What was the person's first job or work experience?

What obstacles did the person overcome?

Early Achievements

What was the person's most important early success?

What processes does the person use in his or her work?

Which of the person's traits were most helpful in his or her work?

Person Today

Has the person received awards or recognition for accomplishments?

What is the person's life's work?

How have the person's accomplishments served others?

Test Yourself

1 Where and when was Laura Ingalls Wilder born?

2 What were the names of Laura's parents?

3 What did Laura call Walnut Grove in her books?

4 What kind of writing did Laura enjoy reading most?

5 What was the lasting effect of Mary's illness?

6 Why was Laura able to recall so many details from her youth?

7 Whom did Laura marry on August 25, 1885?

8 Who encouraged Laura Ingalls Wilder to begin writing?

9 What was the name of the Wilder's farm in Mansfield, Missouri?

10 What television series was based on one of Laura Ingalls Wilder's books?

ANSWERS

1. Laura Ingalls Wilder was born in a log cabin near Pepin, Wisconsin, on February 7, 1867. 2. Caroline and Charles. 3. In Laura's books, Walnut Grove is called Plum Creek. 4. Laura was especially fond of poetry. 5. Mary was left visually impaired. 6. Laura remembered much of her past because she had described her surroundings in detail to her visually impaired sister, Mary. 7. Almanzo Wilder. 8. Rose, her daughter. 9. Rocky Ridge Farm. 10. *Little House on the Prairie*.

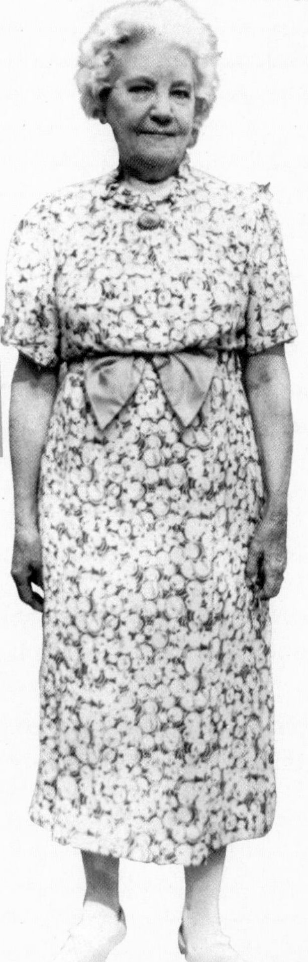

Writing Terms

The field of writing has its own language. Understanding some of the more common writing terms will allow you to discuss your ideas about books.

action: the moving events of a work of fiction

antagonist: the person in the story who opposes the main character

autobiography: a history of a person's life written by that person

biography: a written account of another person's life

character: a person in a story, poem, or play

climax: the most exciting moment or turning point in a story

episode: a short piece of action, or scene, in a story

fiction: stories about characters and events that are not real

foreshadow: hinting at something that is going to happen later in the book

imagery: a written description of a thing or idea that brings an image to mind

narrator: the speaker of the story who relates the events

nonfiction: writing that deals with real people and events

novel: published writing of considerable length that portrays characters within a story

plot: the order of events in a work of fiction

protagonist: the leading character of a story; often a likable character

resolution: the end of the story, when the conflict is settled

scene: a single episode in a story

setting: the place and time in which a work of fiction occurs

theme: an idea that runs throughout a work of fiction

Key Words

diphtheria: an infection that leads to breathing difficulties
homesteader: a person who acquires and settles on new land
homesteading: pioneering; settling on and farming new land
inseparable: always together
literary: relating to writing and books
manuscript: draft of a story before it is published
meningitis: bacterial or viral infection characterized by a high fever and headache
plague: an abnormally large number of pests, such as insects
preserve: to keep from being lost
recite: to repeat something from memory
replica: a scale model of something, such as a building
rival: competitor
scarce: difficult to get or find sod
sod dugout: a rough shelter dug in the ground or the side of a hill
vocabulary: all of the words used or understood by a person or group

Index

Log on to www.av2books.com

AV² by Weigl brings you media enhanced books that support active learning. Go to www.av2books.com, and enter the special code found on page 2 of this book. You will gain access to enriched and enhanced content that supplements and complements this book. Content includes video, audio, weblinks, quizzes, a slide show, and activities.

AV² Online Navigation

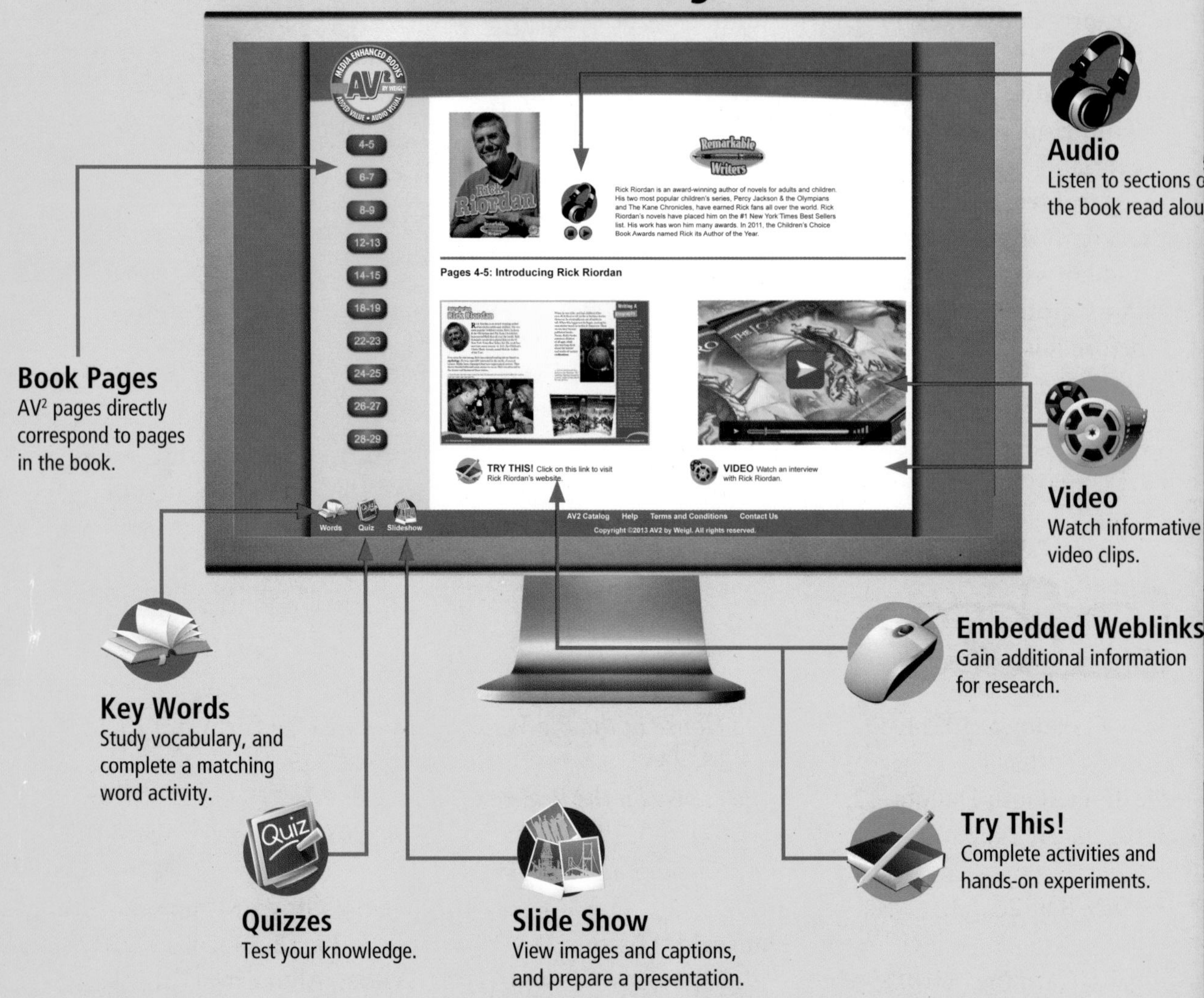

AV² was built to bridge the gap between print and digital. We encourage you to tell us what you like and what you want to see in the future.

Sign up to be an AV² Ambassador at www.av2books.com/ambassador.

Due to the dynamic nature of the Internet, some of the URLs and activities provided as part of AV² by Weigl may have changed or ceased to exist. AV² by Weigl accepts no responsibility for any such changes. All media enhanced books are regularly monitored to update addresses and sites in a timely manner. Contact AV² by Weigl at 1-866-649-3445 or av2books@weigl.com with any questions, comments, or feedback.